Sanjeev Kapoor's

Tasty Eating
for Healthy Living

In association with Alyona Kapoor

- Volume Three -

www.popularprakashan.com

Published by:

POPULAR PRAKASHAN PVT. LTD.

301, Mahalaxmi Chambers

22, Bhulabhai Desai Road

Mumbai 400 026

for **KHANA KHAZANA PUBLICATIONS PVT. LTD.**

(4305)

ISBN – 978-81-7991-557-8

Nutritionist: Kirti Masurkar

Book Design: Pratibha Gurnani Creative

Photography: Bharat Bhirangi, Alim Bolar

Food Stylist: Anupa Das

Printed in India

Standard Press (India) Pvt. Ltd.,

34G, Poothayammal Nagar,

Near YRTV School, Sivakasi - 626 123.

contents

my journey to fitness

I tried to get back to my former slim self for a number of years. When the forties came and settled down comfortably around my waist, I realised that I was not doing much to fight the flab! That's when I decided to begin my 'battle of the bulge'. I have not looked back since! Now I feel good, extremely energetic and really light on my feet, with all that undesired baggage off!

Losing weight is difficult and maintaining an ideal weight is even more difficult. As you read these books you will realize that the emphasis is not on becoming reed thin or a body-building champion, but on eating well-prepared *ghar ka khana*. Just as eating nutritious food is important, exercising is important too.

When I look into the mirror now, I see a confident person who has walked the talk and actually practises what he preaches. Becoming fit is a matter of changing one's attitudes and lifestyle.

why diets don't work!

If at all someone has to analyze the shortest-lived activity ever planned by a human then that would be 'going on a diet'!

We behave quite funnily when it comes to diet. We put faith in the most bizarre notions believing that magic potions and even machines applied for a few minutes every day, will give us a flat stomach. Many of us undergo a painful gastric bypass – anything but make drastic lifestyle changes. The reality is that for most people diets do not work. We go on diets like we go on a holiday. Few people can take a permanent holiday or follow a permanent diet!

Why don't diets work? I noticed two things: in the first month of following a diet, I found a significant weight loss of around three to five kilograms. After that it took nearly six months of persistent dieting to achieve my target. This was because in the beginning the weight loss was more of water and muscle. The fat stores took time to burn off. After you have lost the initial kilos, you reach a plateau and with no further reduction, you tend to slip back into your bad old habits. And now you don't gain back the initial water and muscle you lost; instead you replace it with fat! Uh-oh! With this kind of 'yo-yo' dieting, you become flabbier than when you started out.

The second and most important reason why diets do not work is the lack of lifelong commitment. I have adopted the following principles, and you too can make the changes gradually over a period of time.

my health essentials

O Food quality - eating natural, unprocessed, fresh food.

O Cutting back on the calories.

O Consuming less energy than one can burn off.

O Having more dietary fibre, such as snacking on fruits, consciously.

O Having recommended fats, especially cooking all daily meals in olive oil.

O Having good-quality proteins, like fish (grilled or steamed), four to five almonds, an egg-white omelette and soy milk.

O Emphasizing on complex carbohydrates, having *roti* instead of bread, having brown bread instead of white bread, making *pulaos* and *khichdis* and steamed rice only with brown rice.

O Looking after micronutrient intake - having the recommended daily dose of vitamins and minerals.

my brownie points

O I have tea and coffee without sugar.

O I have fruits for breakfast and also as dessert after meals.

O I have a small snack like a brown bread sandwich before a party, so that I do not reach there absolutely ravenous.

O I bring home-made lunch to office. No take-outs.

O I go for early morning brisk walks.

O I exercise in my home gym with my trainer, which is as essential as a shower!

O I say an emphatic 'no' to second servings at parties when the host/hostess insists too much.

O I climb stairs whenever possible leaving the elevator for other people's use!

What have I achieved? I have achieved an ideal weight with a strong body and good muscle tone, high energy levels and an overall sense of well-being.

After reading this book, I am sure you will achieve the same!

aincourse non-vegetarian

sizzling singapore chilli bean curd

Ingredients

200 grams bean curd
2 tablespoons olive oil
8-10 small onions, halved
1 inch ginger, chopped
5-6 garlic cloves, chopped
4 fresh red chillies
2 tablespoons soy sauce
2 tablespoons hot and sweet sauce
1½ cups Vegetable Stock (Vol. 5, page 66)
½ tablespoon vinegar
Salt to taste
2 teaspoons cornflour
2 eggs

Method

❶ Cut the bean curd into one-inch square pieces.

❷ Heat the oil in a wok. Add the onions, ginger and garlic and stir-fry. Add the bean curd and toss on high heat.

❸ Slice the red chillies diagonally. Reserving some for garnish, add the rest to the bean curd mixture. Add the soy sauce, hot and sweet sauce, vegetable stock, vinegar and salt and cook on high heat. Add the cornflour mixed with two tablespoons of water and continue to cook till the sauce thickens.

❹ Keep a serving plate ready. Beat the eggs and add to the cooking mixture stirring all the time. Remove from heat and transfer onto the serving plate.

❺ Garnish with reserved fresh red chillies and serve hot.

Different version of scrambled eggs loaded with sauces, chilli and bean curd... perfect for a Sunday brunch!

nasi lamek

Ingredients

1 cup brown rice, soaked
2 tablespoons olive oil
4 tablespoons peanuts
2 inches lemon grass stalk, chopped
1 inch ginger, sliced
2 shallots, sliced
2 cups thin Coconut Milk (Vol. 5, page 67)
Salt to taste
1 medium cucumber, sliced
2 eggs, boiled and sliced

Method

❶ Heat the oil in a non-stick wok and sauté the peanuts till golden. Drain on absorbent paper.

❷ Place the rice in a clay (earthenware) pot, add the lemon grass, ginger, shallots, coconut milk and half a cup of water. Add the salt and cook over high heat till the mixture comes to a boil. Lower the heat, cover and cook till the rice is tender.

❸ Serve hot with fried peanuts, slices of cucumber and boiled egg.

A popular breakfast dish in Malaysia, you can have it for breakfast or for lunch. Brown rice is better than the traditional polished rice as it retains the bran and increases the Vitamin B and dietary fibre.

daab chingri

Ingredients

1 cup small prawns, peeled and deveined
1 small tender green coconut
2 medium onions, finely sliced
4-5 green chillies, slit
¼ cup grated coconut
1 teaspoon ginger paste
1½ teaspoons garlic paste
Salt to taste
¼ teaspoon turmeric powder
¼ cup tender coconut flesh, chopped
½ teaspoon *panch phoron*
Wholewheat flour dough, as required

Method

❶ Slice off an inch from the top of the green coconut; drain the water and scoop out the flesh. Retain the top to use as a lid.

❷ Wash the prawns thoroughly under running water. Drain completely.

❸ Preheat an oven to 220°C/425°C/Gas Mark 7.

❹ In a bowl, mix the prawns, onions, green chillies, coconut, ginger paste, garlic paste, salt, turmeric powder and tender coconut flesh.

❺ Heat a non-stick pan. Add the *panch phoron* and when the seeds crackle, add to the mixture.

❻ Stuff the green coconut with the mixture.

❼ Cover the green coconut with the reserved top slice. Seal the top with wheat flour dough.

❽ Bake in the preheated oven for approximately thirty minutes. Let it stand for ten more minutes.

❾ Open the seal just before serving.

Note: *Panch Phoron* is a mixture of equal quantities of five spices: cumin seeds, mustard seeds, fennel seeds, fenugreek seeds and onion seeds. It is used extensively in Bengali cooking.

Daab Chingri is a popular Bengali prawn preparation with high visual appeal as the prawns are cooked in the whole green coconut. The prawns also absorb the flavour of the coconut.

honey and orange glazed chicken

Ingredients

4 (800 grams) chicken breasts, deboned
1 inch ginger, finely chopped
Salt to taste
2 tablespoons mustard paste
6 tablespoons orange juice
4-6 black peppercorns, crushed
1 teaspoon red chilli flakes
4 tablespoons honey
2 tablespoons lemon juice
8-10 baby onions, peeled
2 medium carrots, thickly sliced

Glaze

½ cup orange juice
¼ teaspoon red chilli flakes
1 tablespoon honey
1 teaspoon mustard paste

Method

❶ In a bowl, mix together the ginger, salt, mustard paste, orange juice, peppercorns, chilli flakes, honey and lemon juice. Marinate the chicken in the mixture for about an hour.

❷ Preheat an oven to 200°C/400°F/Gas Mark 6.

❸ Heat a non-stick pan. Add the baby onions and carrots; mix and roast for two minutes.

❹ Spread the vegetables on a baking tray. Place the marinated chicken over the vegetables along with the marinade.

❺ Place in the preheated oven and allow it to bake till done.

❻ For the glaze, mix together the orange juice, chilli flakes, honey and mustard paste and heat in a non-stick pan till reduced to half the quantity.

❼ Mid-way through the baking, glaze the chicken with the mixture and continue to bake till the chicken is cooked.

❽ Serve hot.

This is one of my favourite oil-free recipes! The strong mustard adds a pungency which goes very well with the honey and orange.

chicken teriyaki with black grapes

Ingredients

4 (150 grams each) chicken breasts, skin removed
4 tablespoons soy sauce
2 tablespoons molasses
Salt to taste
½ teaspoon black pepper powder
2 teaspoons oil
1 cup bean sprouts
Enoki mushrooms, to garnish

Sauce

1 tablespoon olive oil
1 inch ginger, sliced
1 medium onion, finely chopped
½ cup white wine
12-15 black grapes, crushed
1 tablespoon soy sauce
½ teaspoon black pepper powder
Salt to taste
1 tablespoon molasses
2 tablespoons honey

Method

❶ In a bowl, mix together the soy sauce, molasses, salt and pepper powder. Marinate the chicken breasts in this mixture for half an hour.

❷ To make the sauce, heat the oil in a pan. Add the ginger and onion and sauté till golden brown.

❸ Stir in the white wine and cook till the mixture reduces a little.

❹ Add the crushed grapes and continue to cook, stirring continuously, for five to seven minutes till the grapes soften.

❺ Stir in the soy sauce, pepper powder, salt and molasses. Mix well and strain the sauce.

❻ Remove the chicken breasts from the marinade and place them on a grill. Pour some of the marinade over the chicken and add the rest to the sauce.

❼ Brush the chicken breasts with some oil and grill till done.

❽ Pour the strained sauce into a pan and cook again. Add honey and reduce the sauce a little.

❾ Cut the grilled chicken breasts into smaller pieces.

❿ Arrange the bean sprouts on a serving plate. Place the chicken on the sprouts. Pour the hot sauce over and serve with enoki mushrooms.

A Japanese presentation with underlying sweet flavours, highlighted with soy sauce. Grapes are low in saturated fat, cholesterol and sodium and high in Vitamins C and K.

bhuna kukda

Ingredients

1 whole (1 kilogram) chicken, skinned
and cut into 8 pieces
12 garlic cloves
20 dried red chillies, soaked
4-5 cloves
4 green cardamoms
2 inches cinnamon
1 teaspoon turmeric powder
Salt to taste
2 tablespoon rice bran oil
1 teaspoon cumin seeds
½ cup skimmed milk yogurt, whisked
½ cup chopped fresh coriander

Method

❶ Grind together the garlic, red chillies, cloves, cardamoms, cinnamon and turmeric powder to a fine paste.

❷ Rub the paste and salt over the chicken and leave to marinate for two hours in a refrigerator.

❸ Heat the oil in a pressure cooker; add the cumin seeds and when they begin to change colour, add the marinated chicken and sauté over high heat.

❹ When all the moisture has evaporated, add the yogurt with half a cup of water. Seal the cooker with the lid and cook till the pressure is released twice (two whistles).

❺ Remove the lid when the pressure has reduced completely. Stir-fry till the *masala* coats the chicken.

❻ Serve hot, sprinkled with the fresh coriander.

Tender chicken coated with spices is a delight with hot *tandoori roti*. The mustard oil adds a rustic flavour and being heart-friendly it is a value addition to the recipe. The fresh coriander helps to digest the chicken faster! Chicken is a good source of good quality lean protein and it is low in carbohydrates. It is advisable to use chicken without skin.

hara masala murgh

Ingredients

1 whole (1 kilogram) chicken, skinned
and cut into 8 pieces
½ cup chopped fresh coriander
4 tablespoons chopped fresh mint
¼ cup grated coconut,
6 green chillies, seeded and chopped
1 tablespoon rice bran oil
4 large onions, chopped
10-12 curry leaves
1 tablespoon ginger paste
1 tablespoon garlic paste
1 tablespoon roasted cumin powder
1 tablespoon coriander powder
2 tablespoons almond paste
¾ cup skimmed milk yogurt
Salt to taste
¼ cup low-fat cream
1 teaspoon *garam masala* powder

Method

❶ Grind together the fresh coriander, fresh mint, coconut and green chillies to a smooth paste to make green chutney.

❷ Heat the oil in a deep non-stick pan; add the onions and sauté on medium heat till golden brown. Add the curry leaves, ginger paste and garlic paste and sauté for three to four minutes or till the raw flavours disappear.

❸ Add the cumin powder and coriander powder and continue to sauté for two minutes.

❹ Add the chicken and sauté for five minutes.

❺ Add the almond paste and sauté until the oil separates and the gravy leaves the sides of the pan.

❻ Add the yogurt and salt and cook further for three to four minutes. Add the green chutney and cook for two to three minutes.

❼ Finally add the cream and stir the mixture. Check if the chicken is cooked.

❽ Sprinkle the *garam masala* powder and stir. Remove from heat.

❾ Serve hot with *chapatis*.

Home recipes for chicken are always in demand! I love the green colour of this dish. The fresh coriander and fresh mint aid in digestion. The almonds add monounsaturated fatty acids which are good for health.

rendang

Ingredients

700 grams boneless lean mutton
2 medium onions, sliced
4 garlic cloves, crushed
1 inch galangal, sliced
1 inch ginger, sliced
4-6 fresh red chillies, seeded
and sliced
1 inch lemon grass stalk,
bruised and sliced
1 inch fresh turmeric, sliced
(or 1 teaspoon turmeric powder)
1 teaspoon coriander seeds, roasted and
powdered
1 teaspoon cumin seeds, roasted
and powdered
2 kaffir lime leaves
2 cups low-fat Coconut Milk (Vol .5, page 67)
1 teaspoon tamarind pulp diluted in
4 tablespoons water
2 tablespoons dark soy sauce
Salt to taste
8 small potatoes
1 large onion, sliced and sautéed till browned

Method

❶ Cut the mutton into long strips and then into smaller pieces. Place them in a bowl.

❷ Grind together the onions, garlic, galangal, ginger, red chillies, lemon grass and turmeric to a fine paste.

❸ Add the paste to the mutton along with the roasted coriander and cumin powders and mix well. Tear the kaffir lime leaves roughly and add. Cover and leave in a cool place to marinate for half an hour.

❹ Heat the coconut milk, three-and-a-half cups water and tamarind water in a deep wok. Add the marinated mut ton pieces and dark soy sauce and salt. Mix and bring the mixture to a boil. Lower the heat and simmer gently, half covered, for about one-and-a-half to two hours or until the mutton is tender and the gravy thickens.

❺ Add the potatoes and continue to cook. Add some more water if necessary and cook till the potatoes are tender.

❻ Adjust the seasoning, and transfer into a serving bowl. Serve garnished with the sautéed onion.

Simple, spicy and delicious, this dish is perfect for a lazy Sunday brunch. The lean mutton has some of the fat removed, and provides Vitamins A and B and folic acid.

pan-fried pomfret in hot black bean sauce

Ingredients

4 (400 grams) pomfret fillets

Salt to taste

2 tablespoons malt vinegar

2 tablespoons dark soy sauce

4 tablespoons cornflour

3 tablespoons oil

2 spring onions, sliced

1 inch ginger, chopped

2 tablespoons oyster sauce

2 tablespoons hot black bean sauce

7-8 black peppercorns, crushed

1 fresh red chilli, chopped

1 teaspoon sugar

1 cup Fish or Chicken Stock (Vol. 5, 66)

2 stalks spring onion greens, chopped

Method

❶ Mix the salt, one tablespoon malt vinegar, one tablespoon dark soy sauce and three tablespoons cornflour in a bowl. Rub the mixture evenly over the pomfret fillets.

❷ Heat two tablespoons oil in a non-stick pan and sauté the fillets for about a minute or till well done. Drain.

❸ Heat the remaining oil in another non-stick pan. Add the spring onions, ginger, oyster sauce, hot black bean sauce and the remaining dark soy sauce and mix. Add the peppercorns, red chilli, sugar and fish/chicken stock.

❹ Mix the remaining cornflour and malt vinegar in a quarter cup of water. Stir into the sauce and cook till the sauce thickens.

❺ Place the fried fish on a serving plate and pour the sauce over.

❻ Garnish with the spring onion greens and serve hot.

Provides an Oriental touch to your meal... with healthy white meat that is so much in demand now! Serve with steamed rice and extra spring onions.

chicken chettinad

Ingredients

1 whole chicken (1 kilogram),
skinned and cut into 12 pieces
6-8 dried red chillies
¼ cup grated coconut
2 teaspoons poppy seeds
1 teaspoon coriander seeds
½ teaspoon cumin seeds
3 green cardamoms
2 cloves
1 inch cinnamon
½ star anise
1 teaspoon fennel seeds
2 inches ginger, roughly chopped
10-12 garlic cloves
3 medium onions, chopped
2 tablespoons rice bran oil
10-12 curry leaves
3 medium tomatoes, chopped
1 teaspoon red chilli powder
½ teaspoon turmeric powder
Salt to taste
Juice of 1 lemon
2 tablespoons chopped fresh coriander

Method

❶ Roast the red chillies, coconut, poppy seeds, coriander seeds, cumin seeds, cardamoms, cloves, cinnamon, star anise and fennel seeds separately in one tablespoon oil in a non-stick pan and grind to a paste along with the ginger, garlic and one chopped onion.

❷ Heat the remaining oil in a non-stick deep pan and sauté the remaining onions till golden. Add the curry leaves and ground paste and sauté for some time. Add the tomatoes, chilli and turmeric powders and salt to taste.

❸ Add the chicken and mix well. Cook for five minutes, add two cups of water and lemon juice, cover and cook till the chicken is tender.

❹ Garnish with the fresh coriander and serve hot with boiled rice or *parantha*.

A typical coconut and chicken preparation from South East Tamil Nadu, where no recipe is complete without the use of curry leaves. Note here that garlic is used liberally along with fennel seeds. In some regions this dish is cooked without coconut. You may try that variation if you so prefer.

mirchi murgh

Ingredients

4 chicken legs, skinned
1 medium onion, roughly chopped
4 garlic cloves, roughly chopped
2 inches ginger, roughly chopped
5-6 green chillies, roughly chopped
Salt to taste
2 teaspoons lemon juice
2 tablespoons coriander seeds
1 teaspoon cumin seeds
4-5 dried red chillies
1-inch cinnamon stick
4 cloves
4 green cardamoms
1 tablespoon rice bran oil
4 tablespoons tomato purée
¼ teaspoon sugar
2 tablespoons chopped fresh coriander

Method

❶ Cut each chicken leg into two at the knee joint.

❷ Grind the onion, garlic, ginger and green chillies until smooth. Stir in the salt and lemon juice.

❸ Rub the mixture on the chicken pieces. Cover and leave to marinate for four to six hours in a refrigerator. Remove from the refrigerator at least thirty minutes before cooking.

❹ Grind together the coriander seeds, cumin seeds, red chillies, cinnamon, cloves and green cardamoms with a little water to a smooth paste.

❺ Heat the oil in a non-stick pan, add the ground paste and sauté on medium heat for two minutes. Add the tomato purée, salt and sugar and continue to sauté till the oil rises to the surface.

❻ Add the marinated chicken and stir. Cover and cook, on medium heat, till the chicken is done.

❼ Garnish with the fresh coriander and serve hot.

As the name of the dish suggests Mirchi Murgh is spicy but pleasantly so. You can always alter the amount of green chillies according to your tolerance level! Chillies are an excellent source of Vitamin C and capsaicin. They are effective in stimulating and enhancing digestion.

methiwali machchi

Ingredients

1 cup chopped fresh fenugreek
4 (500 grams) black pomfret fillets,
cut into 1-inch pieces
1 tablespoon lemon juice
Salt to taste
2 teaspoons rice bran oil
½ teaspoon mustard seeds
1 inch ginger, chopped
3-4 garlic cloves, chopped
4 spring onions, chopped
1 medium tomato, chopped
3-4 green chillies, chopped
1 medium unripe green mango,
peeled and chopped
¼ teaspoon turmeric powder

Method

❶ Marinate the fish pieces in the lemon juice and salt for fifteen minutes.

❷ Heat the oil in a non-stick pan; add the mustard seeds and sauté till they splutter. Add ginger, garlic and spring onions and stir-fry for two minutes.

❸ Add the fresh fenugreek and sauté for two to three minutes. Add the tomato, green chillies mango and turmeric powder and cook for two minutes, stirring continuously.

❹ Add half a cup of water and continue cooking over high heat, stirring frequently.

❺ When the liquid starts boiling add the marinated fish and adjust the salt. Cover and simmer over medium heat for eight minutes or until the fish is cooked.

❻ Stir gently, check and adjust the seasoning and serve hot.

Salt is an important ingredient from the point of view of health, though it supplies no calories. Salt (sodium in salt, to be more specific) plays a significant role in the maintenance of blood pressure. Today salt is fortified with iodine. Iodine deficiency during the foetal stage may lead to mental retardation and in later life retardation of body growth. It is characterized by the swelling of thyroid gland in the neck.

chengfu chicken

Ingredients

300 grams boneless chicken breasts, skin removed and cut into 1-inch pieces
2 tablespoons dry sherry
4 tablespoons cornflour
1 tablespoon soy sauce
2 tablespoons oyster sauce
¼ teaspoon white pepper powder
1 teaspoon sugar
Salt to taste
2 cups Chicken Stock (Vol. 5, page 66)
2½ tablespoons oil
2-3 garlic cloves, chopped
1 spring onion, sliced
2 medium bunches (500 grams) fresh spinach, shredded
8-10 Sichuan peppers
1 tablespoon white vinegar
1 teaspoon red chilli flakes
1 stalk spring onion greens, sliced

Method

❶ Marinate the chicken in dry sherry for half an hour.

❷ Blend two tablespoons cornflour in half a cup of water. Add the soy sauce, oyster sauce, white pepper powder, sugar and salt to taste to the chicken stock and mix well.

❸ Add the remaining cornflour to the marinated chicken and mix well. Heat two tablespoons oil in a non-stick wok and sauté the chicken for two to three minutes or until light brown in colour. Drain on absorbent paper.

❹ Add the garlic to the oil remaining in the wok, and stir-fry briefly. Add the spring onion and continue to stir-fry for a minute more.

❺ Add the spinach and cook for two minutes on high heat, stirring and tossing continuously. Remove and arrange the spinach on a serving platter and keep warm.

❻ Heat the remaining oil in another non-stick wok, add the Sichuan peppers and immediately stir in the chicken stock mixture.

❼ Add the sautéed chicken and cook for two to three minutes. Stir in the blended cornflour and white vinegar and cook for a minute or until the sauce thickens and coats the chicken.

❽ Pour the chicken over the spinach and sprinkle the chilli flakes. Serve hot, garnished with the spring onion greens.

The various Chinese sauces with the sherry play an important role in providing the authentic Chinese taste to this chicken-and-spinach dish. Serve with steamed rice.

murgh ka mokal

Ingredients

700 grams boneless chicken breasts,
skinned
1 tablespoon rice bran oil
3 medium onions, sliced
1 teaspoon cumin seeds
2 tablespoons ginger paste
2 tablespoons garlic paste
½ cup skimmed milk yogurt, whisked
1 teaspoon red chilli powder
½ teaspoon turmeric powder
Salt to taste
2 tablespoons melon seed paste
1 teaspoon *garam masala* powder
½ teaspoon green cardamom powder
12-15 roasted almonds, slivered

Method

❶ Cut the chicken into half-inch thick strips. Blanch in boiling water for two minutes and drain.

❷ Heat the oil in a non-stick *kadai*; add the onions and sauté over medium heat till golden brown. Add the cumin seeds, stir and add the ginger and garlic pastes mixed with four tablespoons of water. Cook for one minute and remove from heat.

❸ Stir in the yogurt and return the *kadai* to the heat. Cook till the oil separates.

❹ Add the chicken strips and half a cup of water; bring to a boil, lower heat and simmer till the chicken is tender.

❺ Add the chilli powder, turmeric powder and salt.

❻ Remove the pan from heat and stir in the melon seed paste mixed with one-fourth cup of water.

❼ Return the *kadai* to the heat and bring to a boil. Add the *garam masala* powder and cardamom powder, stir well and adjust seasoning.

❽ Serve hot, garnished with the roasted almond slivers.

Murgh ka Mokal is high in protein as only boneless meat of chicken breast has been used. The finishing with roasted almonds enhances the amount of good quality fats in the recipe, as does the addition of melon seeds.

murgh takatak

Ingredients

1 cup chicken mince
2 tablespoons rice bran oil
½ teaspoon cumin seeds
1 medium onion, chopped
6-7 garlic cloves, chopped
1 inch ginger, chopped
2 medium tomatoes, chopped
1 teaspoon red chilli powder
3-4 green chillies, chopped
Salt to taste
2 eggs, boiled and peeled
1 teaspoon *garam masala* powder
2 tablespoons fresh coriander, chopped
1 tablespoon fresh mint, chopped
1 tablespoon lemon juice

Method

❶ Heat the oil on a non-stick *tawa* and add the cumin seeds; when they change colour, add the onion and sauté for two to three minutes. Mix in the chicken mince and sauté for five minutes, breaking up the mince with a metal spatula.

❷ Add the garlic and ginger and sauté for a few seconds. Add the tomatoes, chilli powder and green chillies and cook for a few minutes. Add a little water and cook for five more minutes.

❸ Add the salt and whole boiled eggs. Break the mixture up with a metal spatula.

❹ Add the *garam masala* powder, fresh coriander and fresh mint, and mix well.

❺ Sprinkle with the lemon juice and serve hot directly from the *tawa*.

This name comes from the sound of the spatula (*takatak, takatak*) when it breaks up the chicken on the *tawa*! It cooks fast and tastes perfect with hot *roti*.

green chilli chicken

Ingredients

1 whole (800 grams) chicken,
cut into 1½-inch pieces
1 cup small green chillies
3 green chillies, chopped
2 medium onions, quartered
10 garlic cloves
1½ inches ginger, sliced
½ cup chopped fresh coriander
Salt to taste
2 tablespoons rice bran oil
¾ teaspoon cumin seeds
¼ teaspoon turmeric powder
1 teaspoon roasted cumin powder
2 teaspoons coriander powder
1 teaspoon *garam masala* powder

Method

❶ Grind together the chopped green chillies, onions, garlic, ginger, fresh coriander and salt.

❷ Add the mixture to the chicken pieces and marinate for about half an hour.

❸ Heat the oil in a wok or *kadai*. Add the cumin seeds. When they begin to change colour add the turmeric powder.

❹ Add the marinated chicken and small green chillies and mix well. Add the cumin powder and coriander powder and mix well.

❺ Add the *garam masala* powder and adjust the seasoning. Mix again. Add half a cup of water and mix. Cover and cook on medium heat for eight to ten minutes.

❻ Lower the heat and cook for another eight to ten minutes or till the chicken is cooked.

❼ Serve hot.

I confess that I was surprised that this chicken dish was not at all spicy! I expected it to be really 'hot' with the amount of chillies I had used but it was not so... and this is a good reason why the dish is ideal for a party!

kairi murgh

Ingredients

1 whole (1 kilogram) chicken,
skinned and cut into 2-inch pieces
2 medium unripe mangoes
1½ teaspoons ginger paste
1½ teaspoons garlic paste
Salt to taste
2 teaspoons *garam masala* powder
1½ teaspoons green chilli paste
4-5 cloves
3 teaspoons rice bran oil
2 medium onions, sliced
¼ teaspoon turmeric powder
1½ teaspoons red chilli powder
2 teaspoons coriander powder
2 tablespoons chopped fresh coriander
A few pieces of charcoal

Method

❶ Peel and cut the unripe mangoes into small pieces. Purée half the pieces.

❷ In a bowl, marinate the chicken with half the ginger paste, half the garlic paste, salt, half the *garam masala* powder, half the green chilli paste and puréed unripe mango for about an hour, preferably in a refrigerator.

❸ Place a piece of coal over a gas flame till red hot. Put it into a *katori* and place the *katori* in the bowl with the marinated chicken. Place a few cloves over the coal and pour one teaspoon of oil over. Immediately cover the bowl with a lid and leave it to stand for a few minutes.

❹ Heat the remaining oil in a non-stick *kadai,* add the onions and sauté on medium heat till translucent. Add the remaining ginger paste, garlic paste, green chilli paste and sauté for two minutes.

❺ Add the marinated chicken, turmeric, chilli and coriander powders, remaining *garam masala* powder and chopped unripe mango. Stir well so that the *masala* coats the chicken.

❻ Cook on high heat for five to six minutes. Adjust the salt, add fresh coriander and three-fourth cup of water. Cover and cook for ten to twelve minutes or till done.

❼ Serve hot.

This is a delectable dish, the unripe mangoes flavouring it in a fresh exciting way. I might not travel to Hyderabad as often as I would like to, but this recipe transports me there instantly! Unripe mango is a valuable source of Vitamin C. It also prevents gastro-intestinal disorders.

tisryanche kalvan

Ingredients

400 grams clams
Salt to taste
½ tablespoon lemon juice
1 tablespoon olive oil
2 medium onions, chopped
1 tablespoon minced ginger
1 tablespoon minced garlic
¼ teaspoon turmeric powder
2 tablespoons low-fat coconut milk
½ tablespoon tamarind pulp
2 tablespoons chopped fresh coriander

For the *masala*

2 medium onions, thinly sliced
1 tablespoon olive oil
5-6 cloves
7-8 black peppercorns
1 inch cinnamon
½ teaspoon black cumin seeds
1 teaspoon coriander seeds
3 dried red chillies
2 tablespoons grated dried coconut

Method

❶ Clean and wash the clams, sprinkle the salt and lemon juice and set aside for fifteen minutes.

❷ For the *masala*, heat one tablespoon oil in a pan and sauté the sliced onions until golden brown. In another pan, dry-roast the remaining ingredients for the *masala* individually till fragrant. Mix with the browned onions, add a quarter cup of water and grind to a fine paste.

❸ For the coconut gravy, heat one tablespoon oil in a pan. Add the chopped onions and sauté until light golden brown. Add the minced ginger and garlic and sauté for a few seconds. Stir in the ground *masala* and sauté on a low heat for two to three minutes. Add one-and-half-cups of water and bring to a boil.

❹ Add the clams, turmeric powder, coconut milk and tamarind pulp. Cook, covered, for five to seven minutes.

❺ Serve hot, garnished with the fresh coriander.

This dish perhaps epitomises Konkan cuisine. The flavouring from each ingredient is very subtle, but the depth of the blend is what clicks with seafood-lovers like me. Serve with steamed brown rice or wholewheat *roti*, *dal* and vegetables.

keema matar

Ingredients

½ kilogram minced mutton
½ cup green peas, boiled
2 tablespoons rice bran oil
2-3 green chillies, sliced
1 teaspoon cumin seeds
2 large onions, chopped
½ tablespoon ginger paste
½ tablespoon garlic paste
2 medium tomatoes, chopped
Salt to taste
1½ tablespoons red chilli powder
1 tablespoon coriander powder
¼ teaspoon turmeric powder
½ teaspoon *garam masala* powder
2 tablespoons chopped fresh coriander
Lemon wedges, to serve

Method

❶ Heat the oil in a non-stick pan; add the green chillies and sauté for half a minute. Add the cumin seeds and when they begin to change colour, add the onions and sauté till golden brown.

❷ Add the ginger paste and garlic paste and sauté for a minute. Add the tomatoes and salt. Cover and cook on low heat for two to three minutes.

❸ Add the chilli, coriander and turmeric powders and continue to cook for another minute.

❹ Add the minced mutton, sauté for two minutes, add half a cup of water, stir and cover and cook on medium heat for fifteen to twenty minutes or till the mutton is tender, water has evaporated and oil rises to the surface.

❺ Stir in the peas and *garam masala* powder and cook for a minute. Serve hot garnished with the fresh coriander and lemon wedges.

I remember as kids, my siblings and I used to take turns to stir the minced mutton while it was being sautéed in oil. Minced mutton being a good source of calories, protein and fat, it is advisable for those whose demands for energy, protein and fats are more. The green peas increase the nutrient value of this dish manifold.

nalli nihari

Ingredients

500 grams lamb marrow bones
2½ tablespoons *nihari masala*
1½ tablespoons rice bran oil
2 medium onions, sliced
1 tablespoon pure ghee
½ inch ginger, cut into thin strips
2 tablespoons wholewheat flour
Salt to taste
1 tablespoon lemon juice
2 tablespoons chopped fresh coriander

Method

❶ Heat the oil in a non-stick pan and sauté the onions till golden. Drain on absorbent paper.

❷ Heat the ghee in a non-stick pressure cooker. Add the marrow bones and *nihari masala* and sauté for two minutes. Add four cups of water, close the lid and cook till pressure is released eight times (eight whistles). This may take about half an hour.

❸ Remove the lid when the pressure has completely reduced and transfer the contents into a *kadai*. Bring the mixture to a boil. Add half the sautéed onions, and half the ginger and simmer for two minutes.

❹ Combine the wholewheat flour with six tablespoons of water and mix well till smooth. Add to the marrow mixture and continue to simmer till the gravy thickens.

❺ Add the salt and stir in the lemon juice.

❻ Serve, garnished with the remaining sautéed onions, remaining ginger and fresh coriander.

The word *Nihari* means 'fasting' and that is where this dish gets its name. It is cooked overnight and eaten at the crack of dawn, especially during the month of Ramadan when the Muslims eat this for their *sehri* before embarking upon the day-long fast. The lean leg cuts of lamb are a good source of calcium and Vitamins A and D.

tamatar diye machch

Ingredients

2 large tomatoes, grated
2 pomfrets (300 grams each), cut into 1½-inch thick slices
½ teaspoon turmeric powder
1 teaspoon red chilli powder
Salt to taste
2 tablespoons rice bran oil
4 green chillies, slit
2 dried red chilies, broken
2 tablespoons chopped fresh coriander

Panch phoron
¼ teaspoon mustard seeds
¼ teaspoon cumin seeds
¼ teaspoon fenugreek seeds
¼ teaspoon fennel seeds
¼ teaspoon onion seeds

Method

❶ Mix together the turmeric powder, chilli powder and salt. Rub the mixture over the fish and marinate for fifteen minutes.

❷ Heat the oil in a *kadai* and lightly sauté the marinated fish for two to three minutes. Drain on absorbent paper and set aside.

❸ To the same oil, add the *panch phoron* and green chillies and sauté till fragrant. Add the tomatoes and sauté for two minutes. Add the red chillies and continue to sauté for two minutes on high heat.

❹ Add one-and-a-half cups of water and bring the mixture to a boil. Add the fish and salt and cook till the fish is tender.

❺ Garnish with the fresh coriander. Serve hot with boiled rice.

I would label this dish as heart-friendly: fish is excellent and so is the essential oil in the seeds used in the *panch phoron* mix.

murgh zafrani do pyaza

Ingredients

800 grams chicken on the bone,
cut into 1-inch pieces
A generous pinch of saffron
10 almonds, roasted
1 tablespoon melon seeds, roasted
1 tablespoon *chironji*, roasted
1 tablespoon poppy seeds, roasted
2 tablespoons rice bran oil
2 medium onions, sliced
3 teaspoons ginger paste
1 teaspoon garlic paste
3 teaspoons red chilli powder
1 teaspoon turmeric powder
Salt to taste
1 cup skimmed milk yogurt
3 cups Chicken Stock (Vol. 5, page 66)
½ teaspoon *garam masala* powder

Method

❶ Grind together the almonds, melon seeds, *chironji* and poppy seeds to a paste.

❷ Heat the oil in a non-stick pan and sauté the onions till golden. Add the ginger and garlic pastes and sauté for two minutes. Add the chilli powder and turmeric powder.

❸ Add the chicken and sauté for five minutes. Sprinkle a little water at intervals so that the *masala* does not burn. Add the salt.

❹ Add the yogurt and cook further for another minute. Add the ground paste and cook for five minutes stirring continuously.

❺ Add the chicken stock and bring the mixture to a boil. Lower the heat, cover and simmer for twenty minutes or till the chicken is tender.

❻ Add the *garam masala* powder and saffron, stir and remove from heat.

❼ Serve with *paranthe*.

Chicken in an almond-rich gravy finished off with a generous pinch of saffron. As rich as it comes for some palates crave for it! All the seeds used are high in antioxidants, Vitamin B and dietary fibre.

tamatar murgh kofta

Ingredients

5-6 medium tomatoes, quartered
4-5 (600 grams) boneless chicken breasts,
skin removed
1 green chilli, chopped
¼ cup chopped fresh coriander
Salt to taste
1 medium onion, sliced
1½ tablespoons ginger paste
1 tablespoon garlic paste
1 teaspoon red chilli powder
2 teaspoons coriander powder
1 teaspoon cumin powder
1 teaspoon olive oil
½ teaspoon mustard seeds
8-10 curry leaves
2 teaspoons rice flour
½ teaspoon *garam masala* powder

Method

❶ Roughly cut the chicken breasts into small pieces, mince along with the green chilli, half the fresh coriander and salt, until smooth and fine.

❷ Divide the minced chicken into ten to twelve equal portions, shape into balls and refrigerate until required.

❸ Pressure-cook the tomatoes for five to six minutes, along with the onion, ginger and garlic pastes, the remaining fresh coriander, chilli powder, coriander powder and cumin powder and one cup water. Remove the lid once the pressure has reduced completely and cool the contents to room temperature. Purée in a blender till smooth.

❹ Heat the oil in a non-stick pan and add the mustard seeds. When they start to splutter, add the curry leaves and stir-fry briefly. Stir in the tomato purée and one cup of water and bring to a boil.

❺ Lower the heat and gently slide in the prepared chicken balls. Cover the pan with a tight-fitting lid and simmer for fifteen minutes.

❻ Dissolve the rice flour in quarter cup of water and add to the pan, stirring continuously. Simmer for five minutes, add the *garam masala* powder and serve hot.

These are really simple to make and great for a party. Just make sure that you mince the chicken very finely – that way the *koftas* hold together while being cooked. Coriander seeds and other spices contain a good amount of folic acid. Folic acid is required for the multiplication of red blood cells.

dahi methi murgh

Ingredients

1 cup skimmed milk yogurt, whisked
¼ medium bunch (75 grams) fresh fenugreek, chopped
900 grams chicken on the bone, skinned and cut into 8 pieces
Salt to taste
2 inches ginger
5 green cardamoms
1 black cardamom
5 cloves
1 inch cinnamon stick
1 bay leaf
1-2 blades of mace
2 large onions, chopped
20 garlic cloves, chopped
3 green chillies, seeded and chopped
½ teaspoon turmeric powder
1 teaspoon coriander powder
1 teaspoon red chilli powder
2 medium tomatoes, chopped
1 tablespoon dried fenugreek, crushed
1 tablespoon chopped fresh coriander

Method

❶ Mix together the whisked yogurt and salt in a large bowl. Add the chicken and marinate for about thirty minutes. Finely chop half the ginger and cut the rest into strips. Set aside.

❷ Heat a non-stick pan. Add the green and black cardamoms, cloves, cinnamon, bay leaf and mace, and roast over a medium heat until fragrant.

❸ Add the onions and cook until they turn golden brown. Stir in the garlic, chillies and finely chopped ginger and cook for two minutes.

❹ Add the turmeric, coriander and chilli powders to the pan, along with quarter cup of water. Stir and cook for thirty seconds. Add the tomatoes and cook until soft.

❺ Add the marinated chicken and fresh fenugreek and mix well. Cover and simmer until the chicken is almost tender.

❻ Sprinkle the dried fenugreek, ginger strips and fresh coriander. Keep the pan covered for about five minutes before serving.

Another favourite in my home, this recipe is effortless but produces a dish fit for a king – the flavours of the fresh fenugreek (*methi*) and mild spices seep wonderfully into the chicken, thanks to the marination in yogurt. It is also a great way to cook without fat. Serve with rice or *roti*, vegetables and a salad.

chops do pyaza

Ingredients

1 kilogram lamb chops
4 large onions
4 tablespoons rice bran oil
1-inch cinnamon stick
10 green cardamoms
10 cloves
2 teaspoons garlic paste
2 teaspoons ginger paste
1 tablespoon coriander powder
2 teaspoons roasted cumin powder
6 tablespoons skimmed milk yogurt, whisked
½ teaspoon red chilli powder
Salt to taste
½ teaspoon *garam masala* powder

Method

❶ Cut three onions in half vertically and then slice them finely to get half rings. Chop the remaining onion finely.

❷ Heat the oil in a deep non-stick pan; add the finely sliced onions and sauté till they turn golden. Drain on absorbent paper.

❸ Add the cinnamon, cardamoms and cloves to the oil remaining in the pan and stir-fry on medium heat till fragrant. Add the lamb chops, a few at a time and stir-fry till golden brown. Drain and place them in a bowl.

❹ Add the chopped onion to the same pan and sauté till golden. Add the garlic and ginger pastes and sauté on medium heat till the oil separates. Add the coriander powder and cumin powder and continue to sauté for half a minute.

❺ Add the yogurt, one tablespoon at a time, and sauté till it blends well with the rest of the *masala*.

❻ Add the lamb chops, one-and-a-half cups of water, chilli powder and salt. Mix well and bring the mixture to a boil. Cover the pan, lower the heat and cook for about forty-five minutes until the lamb is tender. If the mixture becomes too dry add another half a cup of water.

❼ Add the sautéed onions and *garam masala* powder and mix well. Adjust seasoning. Continue to cook, uncovered, for another two to three minutes, stirring gently.

❽ Serve hot.

Note: You can prepare the dish in advance and reheat just before serving.

Cooking chops can be a lengthy process. Choose fresh meat, marinate perfectly and be assured of a tender finished product.

exercise for health

Exercise is as important as brushing your teeth and bathing daily. So spend at least thirty minutes every day exercising. You will burn calories, keep your bones and muscles strong, improve your balance and reduce stress. The heart beats stronger and improves blood circulation and lungs function better.

Exercising releases a chemical endorphin that creates a feeling of well-being. To make sure you stay flexible, warm up for at least ten minutes by doing stretching exercises, and when you finish exercising cool down and then stretch again. Stretching decreases muscle soreness after exercise, helps your muscles recover from exercise quicker and decreases injuries.

You should change your exercise routine every six to eight weeks, otherwise the body adapts to the changes in muscle tone and one could stop seeing results. Suppose you are on a running routine, switch to walking after six weeks. If you are weight training, consult your instructor for a change in the number of repetitions or the amount of weights. Try to vary the intensity of the exercise. Your body likes change and responds to it as the muscles which are under-utilised, get a good workout.

For exercise to be effective, it must meet certain criteria:

Intensity: The intensity of the exercise is extremely important. When too low, small gains in condition occur and when too high, the risk of injury increases. See that exercise is vigorous but not exhausting. You can measure your pulse rate while exercising and accordingly follow a regime suitable for your heart rate. Don't ape others as what is good for them may not be good for you.

Duration: At least thirty minutes of exercise is advisable. If you are seeking a higher level of fitness, then the duration and frequency can be increased accordingly.

Frequency: One should exercise at least three to five times in a week. People who exercise daily should keep a day of rest to let the body recoup and undergo repair.

choose a regime

A good workout is one which maintains your fitness level, teaches proper breathing techniques and is designed for your body. A wrong exercise regime can result in injury, bad posture and deterioration of the bone and muscle.

Cardiovascular/aerobic exercise

Aerobic exercise involves the continuous movement of large muscle groups where your muscles use oxygen. Aerobic exercise can be sustained for hours because you are exercising at a moderate intensity. You could choose dancing, basketball, bicycling, hockey, jogging, karate, rowing, football, swimming, tennis or fast walking. The latest activity is kickboxing, which combines elements of boxing, martial arts and aerobics to provide overall physical conditioning and toning.

Weightlifting or anaerobic exercise

Anaerobic exercise involves muscular effort, usually short bursts followed by rest. For example sprinting and weight training. Anaerobic exercise builds your muscles and makes you stronger With anaerobic exercise your muscles feel tired and slower and harder to move. Why is this? The contracting muscles are not using a high amount of oxygen to assist in taking away the by products of exercise. Anaerobic exercise cannot be sustained for long periods because of this build-up. As your muscles get stronger, you can be more active for longer periods of time. Stronger muscles hold joints (where two bones meet) together and help protect you from injuries. As you progress, your flexibility improves.

Power Yoga

Power yoga is becoming increasingly popular as a healthy way to burn calories, shed excess pounds and stay fit. You learn to use your body, breath and mind to stretch, relax and energize yourself.

Walking

Walking will help to strengthen leg, back and stomach muscles, will build stamina and will definitely help with weight-loss. You should walk daily, if possible, for as long as you are able to. If you walk for a longer time than is comfortable, you will burn non-fat tissues such as muscle. If you walk for a shorter time than is comfortable, you will not be burning any fat, so it is important to choose the optimum time.

the physiology of exercise

Have you ever wondered what happens inside your body when you exercise? And what occurs when you intensify your workout? You feel pain when you intensify your workout but do you know why? Your body is comprised of three primary systems that work in a tightly-orchestrated fashion to drive everything you do. These systems become particularly impressive as a team when you exercise, or stress your body.

❶ First is your cardiovascular system, that is, the heart and more than 1 million kilometres of blood vessels. The primary purpose of this system is to deliver oxygen and nutrients to your body, while concurrently removing waste products, such as carbon dioxide. The heart is an astonishing piece of machinery that pumps unremittingly, fifty and ninety times a minute from the moment you are born to the day you die. But, if it isn't properly cared for, the heart can be a major source of ill-health. The good news is that physical activity is very good for your heart.

❷ Second is your respiratory system, that is, the lungs that draw in and process oxygen from the air and deliver that oxygen to your bloodstream. Your lungs also expel carbon dioxide, which is the by-product of cellular metabolism.

❸ Third is the musculoskeletal system: your muscles, ligaments and bones. When your muscles contract, your bones, acting as levers, get you moving.

systems at work

At rest, your cardiovascular and respiratory systems are working just minimally, to sustain vital bodily processes. Your musculoskeletal system is largely inactive until you rise from the couch to get a sandwich. As you begin to exercise, everything 'gets energised' and a miraculous cascade of events is set in motion. As you set out on your brisk morning jog, the 'command' to move is an automatic one: your brain sends messages to your muscles to contract. As they do, your bones 'locomote' your body. At rest, your muscles require negligible oxygen and nutrients, but as you begin moving, that demand rises. The command centre, your brain, gets word to the respiratory system: 'We need more oxygen.' What happens? Your respiratory rate climbs. As you inhale, oxygen swirls into your lungs where it is drawn into a maze-like structure, finding its way down into the deepest, smallest areas of your lungs, which are air sacs called alveoli. It is there that the oxygen is passed into your bloodstream.

Now, the heart is called upon to act. To meet the increased muscular demand for oxygen and nutrients, your heart pumps the oxygenated blood to your working muscles at an accelerated pace. Your heart rate rises and drives the fresh blood through your arteries and into your capillary beds where your muscles are 'fed' the necessary oxygen and nutrients that allows them to continue working efficiently. The by-products of muscular exertion are known as 'metabolic waste,' such as carbon dioxide and lactate. The blood promptly carries all this away.

At rest, a 70-kg person has an energy expenditure of roughly 1.2 calories per minute. That's not good news for someone who eats double burgers and does not exercise. The good news is that during exercise, your energy expenditure rises a magnificent twenty-fold! That's why physical activity is imperative for a successful weight-loss program. As you push harder, your three systems work at an accelerated rate: muscles require more oxygen and fuel, respiratory rate and heart rate climb. Eventually, a point is reached at which your body, depending on your level of fitness, will become overwhelmed. The manifestation of this is that 'heaving' pain you feel all over your body. The lactic acid, the by-product of muscle metabolism, begins to build-up - that's the distinct burn you feel.

food tips

Experts now recommend that one should not eat for at least fifteen minutes after exercise. After the lapse of fifteen minutes the body is all set to replace the glycogen in the muscles and liver rather than converting it into fat. Also eating high-calorie foods towards the end of the day makes burning them off difficult. Actually some carbohydrates like fruit juice and curd are best eaten following exercise because your body is looking for a source of energy. If you are exercising regularly follow a healthy eating plan that includes adequate fluid intake.

❶ Have a glass of low-fat milk, or eat another source of dairy (yogurt, cheese, paneer) with every meal, aiming for about 1,000 mg of calcium per day if you are less than fifty years old or 1,200 mg if you are older.

❷ Hydrate regularly. Do not wait till you are thirsty. Exercising dulls your thirst receptors, so make sure you drink before, during and after exercise - whether you feel thirsty or not. A good rule of thumb is to drink half a cup to one cup of fluid every twenty minutes while exercising. To be safe, keep drinking even after your thirst is quenched.

❸ Do not ignore fat completely. A super-low-fat diet is not recommended for those who work out. Instead, women should maintain a low-to medium-fat diet with twenty-five per cent of their calories coming from fat, mostly in the form of monounsaturated and polyunsaturated fats.

❹ Avoid overloading protein. Regular walkers need just 1.4 grams of protein per kilogram of body weight each day.

weave exercise into a busy day

What is in extreme shortage universally? Time! As much as you would like to start exercising and get in better shape and health, you may find it difficult to find the time on a regular basis.

❶ Do it in slots

Break it up. If you cannot exercise continuously for a hour, you will still benefit by working out for just ten to fifteen minutes at a time. Find two or three short periods in which to exercise during your day.

❷ Take an appointment

With yourself! If you are a stickler for schedules, then schedule time for fitness too.

❸ Convenience counts

Go easy on yourself. Find a place to work out that is close to you and convenient. You can exercise at home with a simple set of hand weights or on a staircase.

❹ Morning is best

Do it early in the day. If you leave your fitness routine for the end of the day, it will usually be impossible because of a prolonged meeting or traffic delay. Get up and go first thing in the morning. It is a great way to start your day.

❺ Use the lunch hour

Eat a light home-made lunch and instead of sitting and chatting afterwards, go for a short walk.

❻ Use the weekends

Make weekends count. If you struggle to squeeze in short periods of exercise during the week, schedule an hour per day on Saturday and Sunday for longer activities.

❼ Multi-task

Do two things at once. If you simply cannot turn off the TV, do floor stretches or step-ups in front of the TV.

❽ Walk when you can

Stand when you can sit, sit when you can lie down, walk when you can stand... these minor activities do help to limber you up. If you are likely to have a long chat on the phone try walking while talking. It is possible with mobile phones now.

how can one exercise smarter?

❶ Run on the roads early in the morning before the traffic starts (yes, it could mean you have to be up before 6 a.m.!).

❷ In the gym, wear light-coloured, loose, absorbent clothing.

❸ Do not engage in strenuous workouts, even in a heated pool (you can get overheated and dehydrated in water.)

❹ Carry a frozen water bottle in the pocket of your shorts when on a long run or jog. It helps to keep you cool as well as serves as a thirst quencher.

❺ If you want to do stretching exercises outdoors, or on a daily walk seek shaded areas and pathways. This holds true for joggers and runners too.

❻ Exercise moderately – 60% to 70% of maximum heart rate. Take breaks.

❼ Drink a couple of cups of room temperature water before leaving for the gym or run and have more when returning. If you are a serious long distance runner, have a cup or two of water every twenty minutes.

❽ If it is too hot outside, forget the jog or run and decide to use the gym instead.

❾ If the heat gets you, you need to cool off and fast! Sponge yourself with cool, wet cloths, drink sips of water, stand in the shade… the idea is to lower the temperature as quickly as possible. A heat stroke can be dangerous if left untreated. If you feel suddenly tired, sick, headachy, thirsty, or faint you may be having a heat stroke.

❿ For those who still want to exercise as they did when they were in their twenties but are actually nearing the forties, slow down. Aging can't be avoided, but injuries can. And doctors say that doesn't mean all avid joggers must hang up their running shoes… it's all about exercising smarter. It's a matter of being educated in how to exercise appropriately and what signs to look out for when exercising, like muscle soreness and joint pain.

⓫ Warm up and stretch before jumping into a workout. The larger your range of motion, the further the joint can move before you tear something.

⓬ When exercising always take advice regarding diet and plan your intake for the day. A weekly menu provided by the diet expert will help you get in shape faster.

what's the best time of day to exercise?

Mornings

Pros: The majority of people who exercise or walk consistently do so early in the day. There are fewer distractions and schedule interruptions. Early morning exercise raises your heart rate and metabolism to burn more calories and gives a feeling of physical energy for hours.

Cons: Body temperature is at its lowest one to three hours before awakening, making morning a time of naturally lower energy and blood flow. Cold, stiff muscles may be more prone to injury - be sure to warm up well before doing a higher intensity workout.

Noon and break time

Pros: It can easily become a habit to walk and exercise at lunch time and break time and one can use a walking and exercise partner at work, school, or in your neighbourhood. Body temperature and hormone levels are higher than first thing in the morning. A walk at noon can help regulate the amount of food you feel like eating for lunch, can help you avoid break-time snacking! The exercise will improve blood flow to the brain so you are sharper in the afternoon.

Cons: Time limits may not allow you to get in a full workout - any amount is good, but best if you can walk for thirty to sixty minutes or more at a stretch. Distractions and other commitments make keep you from walking and exercising at the appointed times.

Afternoon and after work

Pros: Research shows afternoon (3-7 pm) to be the best time to exercise for both endurance and for building muscle. For most people, body temperature and hormone levels peak at 6 pm. Exercising three hours before or after the peak will give you your best workout for both endurance and building muscle. Research also shows lung function is best at 4-5 pm and muscles are warm and flexible. After work walking can help regulate the amount of food you feel like eating for dinner.

Cons: Distractions and commitments keep you from walking and exercising at the appointed times. One needs to allow one to three hours to wind down after walking or exercise to be able to fall asleep.

In conclusion: the very best time

The best time to exercise is the time that will fit best into your schedule so you can do it consistently. Experts agree that it is not the time of day that matters as much as finding the time you can set aside consistently for your workouts for the best results. The motivation has to come from within you!

gongura chicken

Ingredients

1 whole (800 grams) chicken, skinned and
cut into 8 pieces
20-25 *gongura* leaves, chopped
10 garlic cloves
½ inch ginger
6 tablespoons poppy seeds
4 teaspoons rice bran oil
5 green chillies, each broken into 2 pieces
1 teaspoon cumin seeds
4 medium onions, chopped
1 teaspoon red chilli powder
1½ teaspoon *garam masala* powder
2 teaspoons coriander seeds,
roasted and crushed
Salt to taste
2 tablespoons chopped fresh coriander

Method

❶ Grind half the garlic with ginger to a fine paste. Chop the remaining garlic.

❷ Soak the poppy seeds in one-fourth cup of water for half an hour and grind to a fine paste.

❸ Heat two teaspoons of oil in a non-stick pan and stir-fry the garlic, *gongura* leaves and green chillies. Set aside.

❹ Heat the remaining oil in another non-stick pan, add the cumin seeds and sauté till they change colour. Add the onions and sauté on medium heat till golden brown. Add the ginger and garlic paste. Sauté for a minute. Add the chilli powder, poppy seed paste, *garam masala* powder and crushed coriander seeds.

❺ Add the chicken and sauté for three to four minutes. Add two cups of water and salt. Cook, covered for five minutes.

❻ Add the fried *gongura* leaves, garlic and green chillies. Stir and cook, uncovered, for another ten to twelve minutes or till the chicken is cooked.

❼ Serve hot garnished with the fresh coriander.

For the uninitiated in Andhra cuisine, *gongura* is a leafy vegetable with a sour taste. I particularly enjoy the zing it adds to this recipe. *Gongura* leaves prevent anaemia and are a rich source of calcium, beta-carotene, dietary fibre and Vitamin C.

doi machch

Ingredients

600 grams *rohu* fish, cut into 1-inch thick slices
1 cup skimmed milk yogurt
Salt to taste
1 tablespoon rice bran oil
2 bay leaves
4-6 cloves
3-4 green cardamoms
2 small onions, grated
3 green chillies, slit

Method

❶ Whisk the yogurt, add salt and marinate the fish in this mixture for twenty minutes.

❷ Heat the oil in a non-stick *kadai* and add the bay leaves, cloves and cardamoms. Cook for fifteen seconds. Add the onions and sauté on medium heat for five to seven minutes.

❸ Add the chillies and fish along with the yogurt. Bring to a boil. Cover and cook on low heat for seven to eight minutes.

❹ Serve hot.

Some people like this recipe cooked in mustard oil. If you wish to use mustard oil, heat it to smoking point, cool it and then use as normal. *Rohu* is very high in calcium which is required for strong bones.

dahi ka gosht

Ingredients

800 grams boneless, lean mutton, cubed
1½ cups skimmed milk yogurt
3 teaspoons rice bran oil
2 medium onions, sliced
2 teaspoons ginger paste
2 teaspoons garlic paste
5 green chillies, minced
Salt to taste
2 bay leaves
1 teaspoon coriander powder
1 teaspoon cumin powder
½ teaspoon mace-cardamom powder
2 tablespoons chopped fresh coriander

Method

❶ Heat one teaspoon of oil in a non-stick *kadai* and sauté the onions on medium heat till brown. Grind the onions to a fine paste.

❷ Marinate the mutton in a mixture of the yogurt, ginger paste, garlic paste, chillies and salt for one hour, preferably in a refrigerator.

❸ Heat the remaining oil in a pressure cooker and add the bay leaves.

❹ Add the marinated mutton and cook till the gravy comes to a boil. Stir in the coriander powder, cumin powder, browned onion paste and half a cup of water.

❺ Seal the cooker with the lid and cook till the pressure is released six times (six whistles). Remove the lid when the pressure has reduced completely and sprinkle the mace-cardamom powder over the mutton.

❻ Serve hot, garnished with the fresh coriander.

Dahi ka Gosht is a traditional recipe for mutton. The use of skimmed milk yogurt keeps the fat content at moderate levels, as mutton is also rich in fat. It is advisable to use lean mutton.

kosha machch

Ingredients

1 small fish (approx 500 grams), preferably *rohu*
Salt to taste
2 teaspoons turmeric powder
1½ tablespoons coriander seeds
1 teaspoon cumin seeds
3 teaspoons mustard oil
2 medium potatoes, unpeeled and diced
¼ teaspoon onion seeds
5 green chillies, slit

Method

❶ Cut the fish into one-centimetre-thick slices and sprinkle with the salt and turmeric powder.

❷ Dry-roast the coriander and cumin seeds briefly. Cool and grind, with a little water, to a fine paste.

❸ Heat two teaspoons of mustard oil to smoking point in a non-stick pan; take the pan off the heat, cool and then heat the oil again on medium heat. Add the fish slices, a few at a time, and fry for a minute on each side. Drain on absorbent paper and set aside.

❹ Add the potatoes to the pan and sauté for two to three minutes. Drain on absorbent paper and set aside.

❺ Add the remaining oil to the same pan and heat. Add the onion seeds and green chillies and stir-fry briefly.

❻ Add the coriander-cumin paste and cook on low heat for a minute, sprinkling a little water to prevent scorching.

❼ Add the potatoes and half a cup of water and simmer for four to five minutes, or till the potatoes are completely cooked.

❽ Gently slide in the fried fish and simmer for two to three minutes, or till the fish is cooked.

❾ Serve hot with rice.

Chef's Tip: In South Asia, mustard oil is generally heated almost to smoking point before it is used for cooking; this reduces the noxious fumes and the strong smell and taste.

Fresh river fish cooked Bengali style... two greats in one bowl. The first time I tried this dish was at a Bengali friend's home in Kolkata a few years ago, and the taste still lingers in my memory. Cook with ease and enjoy at leisure, just as the Bengalis do. Serve with small amounts of brown rice, *dal* and some vegetables.

fish ambotik

Ingredients

2 medium pomfrets (400 grams each), cut into ½-inch thick slices
Salt to taste
1 teaspoon turmeric powder
1 tablespoon coriander seeds
1 teaspoon cumin seeds
¼ cup grated coconut
2 large onions, chopped
8-10 dried red chillies
1 inch ginger, chopped
8-10 garlic cloves, chopped
5 cloves
2-inch cinnamon stick
1½ tablespoons vinegar
1 tablespoon rice bran oil
4-5 green chillies, slit
1½ tablespoons tamarind pulp

Method

❶ Marinate the fish in the salt and turmeric powder.

❷ For the *masala*, dry-roast the coriander seeds and cumin seeds. Grind the coconut, half the onions, red chillies, coriander seeds, cumin seeds, ginger, garlic, cloves, cinnamon and vinegar with a little water to a very fine paste.

❸ Heat the oil in a non-stick pan. Add the remaining onions and sauté till golden brown. Add the ground *masala* and cook on high heat for two minutes stirring continuously.

❹ Add three cups of water and bring the gravy to a boil. Add the green chillies and stir.

❺ Add the marinated fish pieces and simmer for five minutes. Add the tamarind pulp and adjust the salt. Stir gently and cook on low heat for five minutes.

❻ Serve hot with steamed rice.

Ambo means sour and *tik* means pungent - a Goan favourite, you can also make this dish with mackerels or king fish.

saagwala gosht

Ingredients

600 grams lean mutton on the bone,
cut into 1½-inch pieces
500 grams fresh spinach
Salt to taste
5 green chillies
2 tablespoons olive oil
2 bay leaves
4 cloves
1 inch cinnamon
6 green cardamoms
2 black cardamoms
1 teaspoon cumin seeds
3 medium onions, sliced
6-8 garlic cloves, chopped
1 tablespoon ginger paste
1 tablespoon garlic paste
1 teaspoon red chilli powder
1 inch ginger, cut into thin strips

Method

❶ Blanch the spinach in salted boiling water for one minute. Drain well and grind coarsely together with the green chillies.

❷ Heat the oil in a non-stick pan. Add the bay leaves, cloves, cinnamon, green and black cardamoms and cumin seeds. When the cumin seeds begin to change colour, add the onions. Cook till the onions are translucent. Add the chopped garlic and sauté for a few seconds.

❸ Add the ginger paste, garlic paste, chilli powder and mutton. Cook on high heat, stirring continuously for a few minutes. Add three cups of water and cook covered, on medium heat, for thirty to thirty-five minutes or until the mutton is almost done.

❹ Add the salt and spinach and cook till the mutton is tender and thickly coated with the spinach gravy.

❺ Serve hot, garnished with the ginger strips.

One would think this is best ordered from a *dhaba*. But my recipe here will convince you that it is best made at home!

jhinga do pyaza

Ingredients

16 medium (175 grams) prawns, shelled and deveined
1½ tablespoons olive oil
1 teaspoon cumin seeds
2 large onions, chopped
½ inch ginger, finely chopped
5-6 garlic cloves, finely chopped
4 green chillies, chopped
¼ teaspoon turmeric powder
½ tablespoon coriander powder
Salt to taste
16 whole shallots
2 medium tomatoes, quartered
4 tablespoons chopped fresh coriander
3 tablespoons skimmed milk yogurt
1 teaspoon *garam masala* powder

Method

❶ Heat the oil in a pan and add the cumin seeds. When they begin to change colour, stir in the onions and sauté until they turn golden.

❷ Add the ginger and garlic, sauté for one minute, then stir in the green chillies, turmeric powder, coriander powder and salt. Sauté briefly before adding the shallots, tomatoes and half the fresh coriander. Sauté for two minutes.

❸ Add quarter cup of water and cook for a further two minutes, then stir in the prawns. Cook, uncovered, for three to four minutes or until the prawns are almost done.

❹ Add the yogurt, *garam masala* powder and remaining fresh coriander. Simmer for three to four minutes and serve.

Prawns, like all seafood, are fast to cook, and extremely good to eat. The addition of shallots in this recipe improves the texture of the final dish.
I love this with hot fluffy *roti*. You could serve it with *kachumber* too.

kozhi vartha kari

Ingredients

1 whole (1 kilogram) chicken, skinned
and cut into 16 pieces
2 dried red chillies
2 inches ginger
6-8 garlic cloves
1 teaspoon red chilli powder
1 tablespoon lemon juice
1 teaspoon turmeric powder
Salt to taste
5 teaspoons rice bran oil
2 medium onions, chopped
12-15 curry leaves
3 medium tomatoes, chopped
2 teaspoons coriander powder
1 tablespoon tamarind pulp
1 teaspoon *garam masala* powder
16-18 black peppercorns, coarsely crushed
2 tablespoons chopped fresh coriander

Method

❶ Make a paste of the red chillies, ginger and garlic. Marinate the chicken in the chilli-ginger-garlic paste, chilli powder, lemon juice, turmeric powder and salt for three hours preferably in a refrigerator.

❷ Heat three teaspoons of oil in a non-stick deep pan and sauté the marinated chicken on high heat for four to five minutes or till chicken pieces are dry and a little browned. Remove the chicken and set aside.

❸ Add the remaining oil in the pan and sauté the onions on medium heat till brown. Add the curry leaves and stir well. Add the tomatoes, salt and coriander powder and cook till the oil separates from the *masala*.

❹ Add the chicken and a little water. Cover and cook on medium heat for five minutes or till the chicken is done and the *masala* coats the pieces.

❺ Add the tamarind pulp mixed in half a cup of water. Add the *garam masala* powder. Simmer for ten minutes, stirring occasionally.

❻ Adjust the seasoning and add the peppercorns. Garnish with the fresh coriander and serve hot.

This lip-smacking chicken dish from South India tastes better with the chicken cut into smaller pieces.
I prefer to use small boneless chicken pieces. Black peppercorns rate high as a detoxifier.

haleem

Ingredients

500 grams boneless lean mutton,
cut into ½-inch cubes
½ cup broken wheat
1 tablespoon split skinless black gram
1 tablespoon split Bengal gram
1 tablespoon split skinless green gram
1 cup skimmed milk yogurt
Salt to taste
1 tablespoon rice bran oil
4 large onions, sliced
1 tablespoon green chilli paste
1 tablespoon ginger-garlic paste
1 teaspoon caraway seeds
1 teaspoon black peppercorns
6 cups Mutton Stock (Vol. 5, page 66)
1 tablespoon chopped fresh mint
1 teaspoon *garam masala* powder
1 tablespoon pure ghee
½ cup skimmed milk
A few sprigs of fresh mint
3-4 lemon wedges

Method

❶ Soak the broken wheat for three to four hours in two cups of water. Soak the three different types of gram together in one cup of water.

❷ Marinate the mutton in the yogurt and salt for one hour preferably in a refrigerator.

❸ Heat one tablespoon oil in a non-stick *kadai* and sauté the onions on medium heat till golden. Set aside.

❹ Place the soaked broken wheat and gram in a pressure cooker. Add the marinated mutton, green chilli paste, ginger-garlic paste, caraway seeds and peppercorns. Add the mutton stock and mix well. Add the salt, chopped fresh mint, *garam masala* powder and half the sautéed onions. Cover the cooker with the lid and cook under pressure till the pressure is released six times (six whistles).

❺ Remove the lid when the pressure has completely reduced. Remove the mutton pieces with a slotted spoon and set aside. Process the remaining mixture till smooth. Add the mutton back into the mixture.

❻ Heat the ghee in a non-stick deep pan. Pour the *haleem* into the pan and bring to a boil. Lower the heat and simmer for ten minutes. Adjust the seasoning. Adjust the consistency by adding milk as required.

❼ Serve, garnished with the remaining sautéed onions, fresh mint sprigs and lemon wedges.

A great combination of pulses and mutton... it improves the quality of proteins greatly. This should be given to pregnant and lactating women – it will help them meet the additional demand for energy and proteins.

masala prawns

Ingredients

40 medium prawns (425 grams),
peeled and deveined
1 tablespoon rice bran oil
1 teaspoon cumin seeds
2 medium onions, chopped
1 inch ginger, chopped
2 green chillies, chopped
1 teaspoon red chilli powder
¼ cup chopped fresh coriander
2 medium tomatoes, chopped
4 tablespoons tomato purée
Salt to taste
½ teaspoon sugar
2 teaspoons lemon juice
½ teaspoon *garam masala* powder

Method

❶ Heat the oil in a pressure cooker; add the cumin seeds and sauté till they begin to change colour. Add the onions and sauté till light brown. Add the ginger and green chillies.

❷ Add the chilli powder, half the fresh coriander, tomatoes, tomato purée, salt, sugar and lemon juice, and cook till the oil separates.

❸ Add the prawns with half a cup of water, seal the cooker with the lid and cook over medium heat till the pressure is released once (one whistle).

❹ Remove the lid when the pressure has reduced completely and sprinkle the *garam masala* powder over the prawns.

❺ Serve hot, garnished with the remaining fresh coriander.

Prawns are an excellent source of protein and omega-3 fatty acids and a great way to get iron, zinc and Vitamin E. They are also low in saturated fats and high in potassium, Vitamin B12, and phosphorus.

lagan ka keema

Ingredients

1 kilogram minced lamb
4 onions, sliced
2 tablespoons oil
2 tablespoons poppy seeds
2 tablespoons *chironji*
2 two-inch pieces dried coconut
1 teaspoon allspice
15 cloves
2 one-inch sticks cinnamon
8 green cardamoms
4 black cardamoms
A few saffron threads
2 tablespoons warm skimmed milk
3 tablespoons pure ghee
2 teaspoons caraway seeds
2 tablespoons ginger paste
2 tablespoons garlic paste
4 teaspoons coriander powder
2 teaspoons cumin powder
3 teaspoons red chilli powder
Salt to taste
1 cup skimmed milk yogurt, whisked
4 tablespoons chopped fresh mint
+ 2 sprigs for garnish
4 tablespoons chopped fresh coriander
4 tablespoons lemon juice
1 lemon, cut into wedges
A few pieces of charcoal

Method

❶ Heat the oil in a non-stick pan and deep-fry the onions till golden. Drain on absorbent paper. Grind half the onions to a paste and reserve the rest for garnishing.

❷ Dry-roast the poppy seeds, *chironji* and dried coconut till lightly browned. Cool and grind to a fine paste. Dry-roast the allspice, five cloves, cinnamon, green cardamoms and black cardamoms. Cool and grind to a fine powder. Soak the saffron in warm milk and set aside.

❸ Heat half the ghee in a flat-bottomed non-stick pan. Add the caraway seeds, ginger paste and garlic paste and sauté for two to three minutes or till the raw flavours disappear.

❹ Add the coriander powder, cumin powder and chilli powder and sauté for two to three minutes.

❺ Add the minced lamb and sauté on low heat. Add the poppy seed paste. Cook for four to five minutes. Add salt and stir.

❻ Add the yogurt and simmer for another four to five minutes. Add the fresh coriander and mint, stir and cook for two minutes.

❼ Add the roasted spice powder and mix well. Stir in the lemon juice and mix. Check for seasoning and remove from heat.

❽ Make a well in the centre of the mince and place an onion skin in it. Place a red hot piece of charcoal on the onion skin. Pour the remaining ghee over the charcoal and place the remaining cloves on it. Cover the pan immediately and leave to stand for ten minutes so that the smoky flavours are absorbed by the mince. Remove the charcoal and discard.

❾ To serve, transfer the *keema* into a large serving dish and garnish with the reserved fried onions, sprigs of fresh mint and lemon wedges.

A perfect dish to convey that the guests are special at the *lagan* (wedding)! Minced meat with all the added flavours of spices and seeds is finally rounded up with a smoky flavour. The garnish of fresh mint is important as it acts as a digestive aid.

chao tam - prawns on sugarcane sticks

Ingredients

8 sugarcane sticks, each six inches long
2 tablespoons oil

Fish sauce dip
2-3 fresh red chillies, seeded and sliced
3 garlic cloves
¼ cup sugar
3 tablespoons lemon juice
1 tablespoon vinegar
3 tablespoons fish sauce
Salt to taste

Seasoned prawns
300 grams medium prawns, shelled
and deveined
1 teaspoon salt
¼ cup minced chicken
¼ cup flaked white fish fillet
3 garlic cloves
3 shallots
1 teaspoon sugar
1 egg white, beaten
1 tablespoon fish sauce
1 tablespoon roasted rice powder
¼ teaspoon black pepper powder

Garnish
1 head iceberg lettuce, leaves separated
80 grams rice vermicelli, blanched
and drained (optional)
4 shallots, sliced and crisply fried
A few sprigs of fresh coriander
A few sprigs of fresh mint

Method

❶ To make the fish sauce dip, grind the chillies and garlic coarsely. Add the rest of the ingredients and stir until the sugar dissolves. Set aside.

❷ Rub the salt into the prawns and set aside for fifteen minutes. Rinse and drain.

❸ Grind the prawns, chicken, fish fillet, garlic, shallots and sugar to a paste in a blender. Add the egg white, fish sauce, roasted rice powder and black pepper powder and mix well. Divide into eight equal portions.

❹ Lightly grease your hands and wrap a portion of the prawns mixture tightly around the middle of a sugarcane stick. Repeat this with the remaining mixture and sugarcane sticks.

❺ Heat a grill pan and grill the sticks over medium heat for five to ten minutes, rotating them frequently, until lightly browned on all sides. Remove and place them on a plate.

❻ On individual serving plates, arrange the lettuce leaves, rice vermicelli (if using), fried shallots, fresh coriander and fresh mint. Arrange the prawn sticks over them and serve with the fish sauce dip.

This takes some effort to make but the result is exotic! It is rich in protein, since it contains, fish, egg and minced chicken. The greens provide roughage for healthy digestion.

grilled bangda

Ingredients

8 medium whole mackerels
Salt to taste
2 tablespoons lemon juice
2 inches ginger
12-15 garlic cloves
10-12 *kokum* rinds
3 teaspoons red chilli powder
½ teaspoon turmeric powder
1 cup coarse rice powder
1 tablespoon olive oil

Garnish
1 onion, cut into rounds and separated into rings

Method

❶ Clean and gut the mackerels and wash them thoroughly. Make four to five quarter-inch deep cuts on both sides of each fish, and apply salt and lemon juice. Set aside for fifteen minutes.

❷ Grind the ginger and garlic to a fine paste. Soak the *kokum* in half a cup of warm water for fifteen minutes. Extract the pulp, strain and set aside.

❸ Mix together the chilli powder, turmeric powder, ginger-garlic paste, *kokum* pulp and salt and marinate the mackerels for half an hour, preferably in a refrigerator.

❹ Heat a grill. Roll the fish in rice powder. Brush a little oil on the grill and grill the fish for five to six minutes or till the fish is cooked on both sides and the surface becomes brown and crisp. Baste with a little oil a few times while cooking.

❺ Serve hot, garnished with onion rings.

Mackerel is a tremendous source of high-quality nutrients. It contains omega-3 essential fatty acid that plays an important role in maintaining cardiac health and it acts as an antioxidant too. It should be served to menopausal women.

tandoori chicken

Ingredients

1 whole (800 grams) chicken, skin removed
1 teaspoon Kashmiri red chilli powder
1 tablespoon lemon juice
Salt to taste

Marinade
1 cup skimmed milk yogurt
1 teaspoon Kashmiri red chilli powder
Salt to taste
2 tablespoons ginger paste
2 tablespoons garlic paste
2 tablespoons lemon juice
½ teaspoon garam masala powder
2 tablespoons mustard oil
1 tablespoon butter
½ teaspoon chaat masala

Garnish
Onion rings and lemon wedges

Method

❶ Make incisions with a sharp knife on the chicken breast, legs and thighs.

❷ Apply a mixture of one teaspoon chilli powder, one tablespoon lemon juice and salt over the chicken and set aside for half an hour.

❸ For the marinade, tie up the yogurt in a piece of muslin and hang over a bowl for fifteen to twenty minutes. Place the thick yogurt in another bowl. Add the chilli powder, salt, ginger paste, garlic paste, lemon juice, garam masala powder and mustard oil.

❹ Rub the mixture over the chicken and marinate for three to four hours in a refrigerator.

❺ Thread the chicken onto a skewer and cook in a moderately hot tandoor or in a preheated oven at 200°C/400°F/Gas Mark 6 for ten to twelve minutes, or until almost done. Baste the chicken with a little butter and cook for another four minutes. Remove and set aside.

❻ Sprinkle with the chaat masala powder and serve with onion rings and lemon wedges.

An all-time favourite food enjoyed the world over, Tandoori Chicken is good for building muscles and raising the energy level. Since it is very high in protein it is good for growth and repair of cells and tissues.

masala pomfret

Ingredients

2 (600 grams each) fresh pomfrets
Salt to taste
Crushed black peppercorns to taste
1 teaspoon red chilli powder
½ teaspoon turmeric powder
2 tablespoons olive oil + to shallow-fry
1 tablespoon garlic paste
1 tablespoon red chilli paste
1 tablespoon fresh coriander paste
1 tablespoon tamarind pulp
½ teaspoon clove powder
½ cup rice flour
1 tablespoon chopped fresh coriander
1 medium onion, cut into rings
1 lemon, cut into wedges.

Method

❶ Make one-centimetre deep slits on either side of the pomfrets. Rub the salt, peppercorns, chilli powder and turmeric powder on the pomfrets and marinate for fifteen minutes.

❷ Mix together the olive oil, garlic paste, chilli paste, fresh coriander paste, tamarind pulp, clove powder and a pinch of salt. Rub the marinade on all the sides of the pomfrets and marinate for fifteen minutes.

❸ Heat a non-stick *tawa*. Roll each pomfret in rice flour and place on the *tawa*. Drizzle one tablespoon oil all round the fish and cook for two to three minutes. When the underside is golden flip over, drizzle some more oil all round and cook till the other side is evenly golden.

❹ Garnish with fresh coriander and serve hot with onion rings and lemon wedges.

Fiery yet deliciously flavourful, I could not stop at one helping. A few sips of Solkadi in between mouthfuls gives it an added zing. Pomfret is low in carbohydrates and fat.

palak chicken

Ingredients

2 large bunches (350 grams each)
fresh spinach
1 whole (800 grams) chicken,
skinned and cut into 12 pieces
3-4 green chillies
Salt to taste
1 teaspoon coriander powder
2 teaspoons roasted cumin powder
2 tablespoons rice bran oil
4-5 black peppercorns
3 green cardamoms
2 cloves
1 bay leaf
2 medium onions, chopped
1 inch ginger, chopped
8 garlic cloves, chopped
½ teaspoon *garam masala* powder
3 tablespoons yogurt, whisked
1 teaspoon dried mango powder
1 inch ginger, cut into thin strips

Method

❶ Blanch the spinach leaves in plenty of hot water for two to three minutes. Drain and dip in chilled water. Drain thoroughly. Grind with the green chillies to a smooth purée and set aside.

❷ Apply a little salt, coriander powder and roasted cumin powder to the chicken and marinate for fifteen minutes.

❸ Heat the oil in a non-stick deep pan. Add the peppercorns, cardamoms, cloves, bay leaf and onions and sauté till golden.

❹ Add the ginger and garlic and sauté till fragrant. Add the chicken and *garam masala* powder and mix well. Cook till the chicken is three-fourth done.

❺ Add the spinach purée and mix. Add the yogurt and adjust salt.

❻ Mix well and cook on medium heat till the chicken is tender. Sprinkle the dried mango powder.

❼ Serve hot garnished with the ginger strips.

I have yet to eat as tasty a *Palak Chicken* as the way my father prepared it. He would tell us that it is extremely good for health too since spinach contains good amounts of calcium required for strong bones and beta-carotene which protects the skin, heart and eyes. Combined with the goodness of chicken, this dish makes an excellent energy-giving food.